Hugh Lewin
and Lisa Kopper

A Shell on the Beach

Hamish Hamilton · London

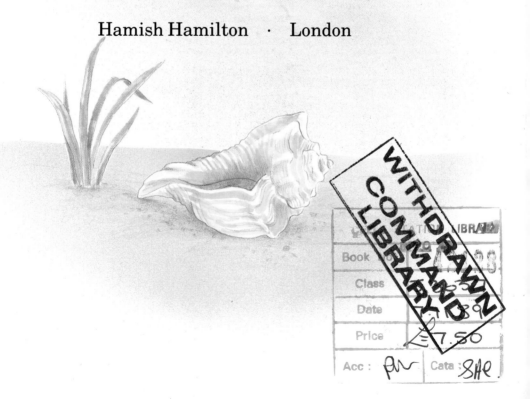

d never been to the sea. Not till last summer.
d read about it, and seen many pictures. But I'd
ever actually *been* there.

ur Uncle Bill was a sailor and he said the sea is big,
ery big. You can see forever, and it's beautiful on the
each, full of sand and sun like in the adverts. All clean
nd fresh-airy, and with lots of space to play in.

There's no sea where we live, or sun,
or trees either. We've got cars and trucks
and tall buildings and people hurrying
everywhere. Lots of noise, and it isn't very
clean. There's often a nasty smell in the air.

We do have the shops in the high street
and a playground on the corner.

When you look out of our window there's
a sea of rooftops, as far as you can see.

Our class went down to the sea in a bus.
I wanted to see the beach.

We left early. We sang through the streets
and the traffic.

We passed rows and rows of houses that
never seemed to end.

We sang all the way, till there was this hill
and we sang up it, then suddenly stopped.
There it was: the sea. It looked lovely
from far away.

But when we arrived we found the sand was dirty, with lots of other muck, and broken bottles, dirty plastic and rubbish.

And the water was all oily. We couldn't even paddle.

DANGER
DO NOT SWIM

We played around on the front for a while and had lunch on the pier.

Before we left, I went on my own to a pool,
down in the rocks, and found a shell.

It's only a small shell – but if you hold it to your ear you can hear the waves breaking on the beach, stretching out with sun and sand, much further than you can ever see.